AMAR CHITRA KATHA

Illustrated Classics From India

Amrapali

Lord Buddha attached more importance to the emancipation of the masses than to the salvation of the individual. His concern for the masses manifested itself in the establishment of the *sangha*, which could be described as an association of seekers.

Amrapali and Vasavadatta were two women disciples of Lord Buddha who gave up their life of pleasure and took to asceticism. At first, the women were not admitted to this order by Lord Buddha, but when his favourite disciples pleaded on their behalf, he relented.

This Amar Chitra Katha comprises of two tales, 'Amrapali' and 'Upagupta'. The dancer Amrapali's conversion to Buddha's sangha is told in the *Maha-Parinibbana Sutta* and in *Malasarvastivadas*. The garden that Amrapali gave up to Lord Buddha was still in existence when Fa-Hien visited India during the Gupta age.

Upagupta was a disciple of Buddha. For him, *ahimsa* (non-violence) did not merely mean desisting from violence, but also indulging in positive acts and showing compassion. When the much-admired Vasavadatta was shunned by society and had nowhere to go, Upagupta took her to his hermitage. While adapting this story, we have omitted a few gruesome details.

Script: Subba Rao   Illustrations: H.S. Chavan and Ranjana

IBH
INDIA BOOK HOUSE

Mahalaxmi Chambers, 5th Floor, 22 Bhulabhai Desai Road, Mumbai 400 026, India.

© India Book House Pvt. Ltd. 2000   Reprinted: June 2005   ISBN: 81-7508-290-9
Printed at Shashi Offset, B-15, Pravasi Ind. Estate, Visweshwar Nager Road,
Goregaon (E) Mumbai - 400 063.

NO. 10022 Rs. 75

Buddhist Tales

3 Illustrated Classics from India
Amrapali • Buddha • Angulimala

AMRAPALI

THE LICCHAVI NOBLES, WHO RULED OVER ANCIENT VAISHALI, WERE GREAT LOVERS OF BEAUTY AND TOOK A KEEN INTEREST IN THE MAINTENANCE OF THEIR GARDENS.

THE BEST OF GARDENERS WAS EMPLOYED TO TEND THE PLANTS.

ONE DAY—

WHAT'S THAT UNDER THE MANGO TREE? WHY, IT'S A LADY! WHAT AN EXTRA-ORDINARY BEAUTY!

HE WENT UP TO HER.

WHO ARE YOU, FAIR LADY? WHAT IS YOUR NAME? WHERE HAVE YOU COME FROM? AND WHAT IS YOUR DESTINATION?

I DON'T HAVE A NAME. I COME FROM NOWHERE AND HAVE NOWHERE TO GO.

ARE YOU GOING TO LIVE IN THIS GARDEN?

YES. IF YOU DO NOT MIND, I WOULD LIKE TO LIVE HERE.

I CERTAINLY DON'T MIND. BUT THIS GARDEN BELONGS TO THE NOBLES. THEY SHOULD BE INFORMED.

LEAVING HER IN THE GARDEN, HE WENT TO THE NOBLES.

A STRANGE LADY HAS APPEARED IN THE STATE GARDEN!

IN ALL VAISHALI THERE IS NO ONE AS BEAUTIFUL AS SHE IS!

WHO COULD SHE BE?

WHY HAS SHE COME HERE?

THEY RUSHED OUT TO MEET THE MYSTERIOUS MAIDEN.

WHEN THEY REACHED THE GARDEN —

THE GARDENER KNEW WHAT HE WAS TALKING ABOUT! SHE IS THE MOST ENCHANTING LADY I HAVE EVER SEEN!

AMRAPALI* SHALL BE MINE!

YOU'LL HAVE TO TAKE HER FROM ME FIRST!

A FIERCE FIGHT BROKE OUT AMONG THE NOBLES. EACH WANTED AMRAPALI FOR HIMSELF!

* THE MANGO-GIRL, AS SHE WAS FOUND NEAR THE MANGO TREE

SUDDENLY —

STOP!

DO I HAVE NO CHOICE IN THE MATTER? CAN I NOT HAVE MY SAY?

WE HAVE BEEN SELFISH, THOUGHTLESS!

YOU CHOOSE ONE AMONG US, AMRAPALI.

THE ONE YOU CHOOSE, SHALL MARRY YOU.

IF I CHOOSE ONE OF YOU, I WILL NO DOUBT BE MAKING HIM VERY HAPPY. BUT I WILL BE MAKING ALL THE OTHERS JEALOUS AND ANGRY. SO I WILL NOT MARRY ANY OF YOU.

THE ELDERS OF VAISHALI, WHO HAD HURRIED TO THE GARDEN ON HEARING THE CLASH, SUPPORTED HER.

A WISE DECISION, INDEED! AMRAPALI CANNOT BELONG TO ONE PERSON. SHE SHALL BELONG TO VAISHALI.

WE AGREE.

AMRAPALI HAS NO PLACE TO LIVE IN. LET US PRESENT THIS GARDEN TO HER.

AND WE COULD HAVE A HOUSE BUILT HERE FOR HER.

AS SOON AS THE HOUSE WAS READY —

THIS GARDEN AND THE HOUSE ARE YOURS, AMRAPALI.

I SHALL EVER REMAIN INDEBTED TO THE PEOPLE OF VAISHALI FOR THE LOVE THEY HAVE SHOWN ME.

TO ENTERTAIN THE NOBLES OF VAISHALI, AMRAPALI, AN EXCELLENT DANCER, BEGAN TO GIVE DANCE PERFORMANCES.

SUCH PERFECT RHYTHM!

SHE IS MATCHLESS!

NO OTHER KINGDOM CAN BOAST OF SUCH AN ACCOMPLISHED DANCER!

SHE IS INDEED, THE PRIDE OF VAISHALI!

ONE EVENING, WHEN THE NOBLES WERE WATCHING AMRAPALI PERFORM, A MESSENGER RUSHED IN.

MASTER! I HAVE BAD NEWS! VAISHALI IS IN DANGER!

THE MAGADHAN ARMY IS HEADING TOWARDS VAISHALI.

WHAT! THAT MONSTER BIMBI-SARA AGAIN!

DUTY CALLS! WE WILL SEE YOU LATER, AMRAPALI.

AS AMRAPALI WATCHED THE YOUNG MEN OF VAISHALI RIDE TO THE BATTLEFIELD —

WHY DO MEN FIGHT? WHAT DO THEY GAIN BY KILLING ONE ANOTHER? ONE MOMENT THEY APPRECIATE BEAUTY AND ART; THE NEXT, THEY THIRST FOR BLOOD.

A FEW DAYS LATER, A STRANGER CALLED ON HER.

WHAT A WINSOME PERSONALITY HE HAS!

I HAVE COME A LONG WAY TO SEE YOU DANCE. WILL YOU DANCE FOR ME, FAIR ONE?

AMRAPALI DANCED FOR HIM.

NO WONDER THE LICCHAVIS ARE PROUD OF HER. WE DON'T HAVE A DANCER TO EQUAL HER IN ALL MAGADHA.

WHEN THE DANCE WAS OVER —

WHERE DO YOU STAY IN VAISHALI?

I AM A STRANGER HERE. I HAVE NOT YET FOUND A PLACE TO STAY.

THEN YOU ARE WELCOME TO STAY AT MY HOUSE.

YOU ARE VERY GENEROUS, AMRAPALI.

THE STRANGER STAYED WITH HER FOR A WEEK. THEN —

AMRAPALI, I MUST TAKE YOUR LEAVE. I HAVE TO GO BACK.

I LOVE YOU, AMRAPALI. WHY DON'T YOU COME AWAY WITH ME?

YOU AMUSE ME. YOU ARE A TOTAL STRANGER. I DON'T EVEN KNOW YOUR NAME!

I AM BIMBISARA.

WHAT! THE DREADED KING OF MAGADHA!

THERE IS NO ROOM FOR LOVE IN THE HEARTS OF AMBITIOUS MEN! HOW CAN YOU TALK OF LOVE, WHEN THIS VERY MOMENT BECAUSE OF YOU HUNDREDS OF MEN ARE DYING ON THE BATTLEFIELD?

A FEW DAYS LATER —

AMRAPALI, WE ARE BACK.

THAT COWARD, BIMBISARA, CALLED OFF THE BATTLE.

WHY DID HE DO IT? WAS IT FOR LOVE OF ME?

AMRAPALI, WE MISSED YOU.

WE WOULD LIKE TO SEE YOU COMPLETE THE DANCE YOU BEGAN, WHEN WE LEFT.

YOU SHALL, IN A MOMENT.

AS AMRAPALI DANCED —

WHAT IS WRONG WITH HER TODAY?

HER MOVEMENTS ARE LIFELESS.

AS THE NOBLES LEFT FOR THEIR HOMES —

AMRAPALI'S PERFORMANCE WAS A FAILURE TODAY.

IT WAS EVIDENT THAT HER HEART WAS NOT IN IT!

MEANWHILE, AMRAPALI SAT BROODING.

WHAT IS THE MATTER WITH ME? WHY DID I FIND NO JOY IN DANCING FOR THE NOBLES TODAY?

WHY DO THE PRESENTS THAT ONCE PLEASED ME, NOW DISGUST ME? WHY DO I FEEL LONELY... LOST... AFRAID...?

THE NEXT MORNING, AS SHE WAS IN HER GARDEN —

WHAT A BEAUTIFUL LOTUS! HOW FRESH IT IS!

WILL YOU SELL THAT LOTUS TO ME, MY LAD?

PARDON ME, LADY. THIS LOTUS IS NOT FOR SALE.

HAVEN'T YOU HEARD? LORD BUDDHA HAS COME TO VAISHALI AND IS CAMPING AT KOTIGRAMA. I AM TAKING THIS FLOWER TO HIM.

AS THE BOY WENT HIS WAY—

LORD BUDDHA! THE ENLIGHTENED ONE WHO KNOWS THE CAUSE OF SUFFERING! I WILL GO TO HIM.

SHE WENT TO KOTIGRAMA.

SHE LISTENED TO LORD BUDDHA WITH RAPT ATTENTION.

OUT OF DESIRE IS BORN GRIEF. OUT OF DESIRE ALONE IS BORN FEAR. FREE YOURSELF FROM DESIRE AND THE GRIEF AND THE FEAR WILL WITHER AWAY.

SHE BEGAN TO EXPERIENCE A NEW KIND OF JOY.

HIS WORDS FILL ME WITH PEACE! HIS VOICE IS SO SOFT! HIS WORDS SO SOOTHING!

SHE WENT TO KOTIGRAMA DAILY. ONE DAY—

HIS VERY PRESENCE STILLS MY RESTLESS MIND. HOW I WISH HE WOULD VISIT MY HOME AND FILL IT WITH HIS BEING!

BUT WILL THE LORD VISIT THE HOUSE OF AN UNWORTHY PERSON LIKE ME?

SOON IT WAS TIME FOR LORD BUDDHA TO LEAVE VAISHALI.

WHEN WILL I SEE YOU AGAIN, MASTER?

EVEN AFTER LORD BUDDHA HAD LEFT, AMRAPALI CONTINUED TO VISIT KOTIGRAMA EVERY EVENING.

THIS IS WHERE THE MASTER USED TO SIT. I CAN STILL FEEL HIS PRESENCE HERE.

MANY MONTHS PASSED. AND AMRAPALI PATIENTLY WAITED FOR THE RETURN OF LORD BUDDHA.

MY MASTER WILL COME TO VAISHALI AGAIN. PERHAPS TODAY, PERHAPS TOMORROW, BUT HE WILL COME.

ONE EVENING —

MY MASTER IS BACK! I CAN'T BELIEVE MY EYES.

SHE RAN UP TO LORD BUDDHA AND FELL AT HIS FEET.

ARISE, MY CHILD.

AND BEFORE SHE COULD STOP HERSELF, THE WORDS POURED OUT.

MASTER, WILL YOU HONOUR ME BY EATING AT MY HOUSE TOMORROW?

I WILL COME, MY CHILD.

AMRAPALI SPED HOMEWARDS TO VAISHALI, TO PREPARE FOR THE COMING OF HER MASTER.

SUDDENLY, A FEW CHARIOTS CARRYING THE NOBLES OF VAISHALI, CAME CHARGING FROM THE OPPOSITE DIRECTION.

WHERE ARE YOU SPEEDING TO?

WE HEARD THAT LORD BUDDHA HAS ARRIVED. WE ARE OFF TO INVITE HIM TO EAT WITH US AT THE PALACE TOMORROW.

BUT THE LORD HAS ALREADY AGREED TO DINE AT MY HOUSE TOMORROW.

WE HAVE BEEN FORESTALLED!

NOT ALL IS LOST. NOT YET. SHE CAN EASILY BE BOUGHT OFF.

AMRAPALI, IF YOU LET LORD BUDDHA HAVE HIS FIRST MEAL AT VAISHALI WITH US, WE WILL GIVE YOU ALL THE GOLD YOU WANT.

NO. EVEN IF YOU OFFER ME THE KINGDOM OF VAISHALI, I WON'T GIVE UP THE HONOUR OF SERVING THE LORD!

AS AMRAPALI DROVE AWAY —

WHAT SHALL WE DO?

WE WILL GO TO THE LORD. HE CANNOT REFUSE THE NOBLES OF VAISHALI.

LATER, AT KOTIGRAMA —

LORD, PLEASE HONOUR US BY DINING WITH US TOMORROW.

I AM SORRY. I CAN'T. I HAVE ALREADY AGREED TO GO TO AMRAPALI'S HOUSE TOMORROW.

THE NEXT DAY, LORD BUDDHA WENT TO AMRAPALI'S HOUSE.

I HAVE COME, AMRAPALI.

LORD, YOU DO ME GREAT HONOUR.

LATER —

LORD, WHY DO I FEEL SUCH IMMENSE JOY AS I SERVE YOU?

AMRAPALI, YOU HAVE BEGUN TO KNOW THE JOY OF GIVING.

LATER —

LORD, PERMIT ME TO GRANT MY GARDEN AND HOUSE TO THE SANGHA.

SO BE IT, CHILD. IT COULD BE USED AS A MONASTERY.

THEN, LEAVING BEHIND HER THE WORLDLY LIFE AND ITS HEARTACHES...

...AMRAPALI BEGAN TO LEAD A LIFE OF RENUNCIA- TION, FINDING AT LAST THE PEACE OF MIND SHE HAD CRAVED.

UPAGUPTA

LONG, LONG AGO IN ANCIENT MATHURA, THERE LIVED A DANCER CALLED VASAVADATTA, WHO WAS FAMED FOR HER BEAUTY AND HER ART.

WHAT A PERFECT FIGURE! WHAT A CHARMING APPEARANCE! WHAT GRACEFUL MOVEMENTS...

...AND WHAT A HARD HEART! SHE'S UNIQUE, INDEED!

YOU SEEM BITTER. HAVE YOU TOO BEEN SPURNED BY HER?

AFTER THE PERFORMANCE, AS VASAVADATTA LEFT THE TOWN HALL —

I AM PREPARED TO PART WITH ALL MY WEALTH FOR A SMILE FROM HER.

WITH NOT SO MUCH AS A GLANCE AT HER ADMIRERS, VASAVADATTA SAT IN HER CHARIOT AND RODE HOME WITH HER COMPANION.

THEY ARE ALL MADLY IN LOVE WITH YOU. COULDN'T YOU SEE IT IN THEIR EYES?

I CHOSE NOT TO SEE.

WHY, VASAVADATTA? WHY DON'T YOU MARRY ONE OF THEM? IS THERE NOT A SINGLE ONE WHOM YOU DEEM WORTHY OF YOUR LOVE?

NO! NOT ONE OF THEM POSSESSES WHAT I AM LOOKING FOR.

ONE EVENING, AS VASAVADATTA WAS STANDING IN THE BALCONY OF HER MANSION, SHE SAW A YOUNG MONK PASS BY IN THE STREET BELOW.

QUICK! RUN DOWN AND INVITE THAT MONK IN.

I CAN'T BELIEVE IT. VASAVADATTA SHOWING SOME INTEREST IN A MAN!

VASAVADATTA WISHES TO SEE YOU, HOLY ONE. WILL YOU COME IN?

NOT NOW. I WILL SEE HER AT THE PROPER TIME.

THE MONK WHO SPURNED THE INVITATION OF THE DANCER, WAS UPAGUPTA, A DISCIPLE OF LORD BUDDHA.

WHEN VASAVADATTA WAS TOLD OF THE MONK'S REACTION —

PERHAPS, HE HESITATES TO VISIT ME BECAUSE HE IS POOR AND CAN'T BRING ME GIFTS. TELL HIM I DON'T WANT ANYTHING FROM HIM.

23

HER FRIEND WENT BACK TO UPAGUPTA.

O MONK, MY FRIEND DOES NOT CRAVE FOR GIFTS OR RICHES. PLEASE VISIT HER.

NO, I CANNOT. IT IS NOT YET TIME TO VISIT VASAVADATTA.

AND UPAGUPTA WALKED AWAY.

VASAVADATTA WAS STUNNED.

WHY SHOULD THE ONLY MAN I CHOOSE TO LOVE, SHUN ME?

SHE STOPPED GIVING DANCE PERFORMANCES, MUCH TO THE ANNOYANCE OF THE PEOPLE OF MATHURA.

WHAT IS THE MATTER WITH VASAVADATTA?

LIFE IN MATHURA HAS LOST ITS CHARM. HOW COULD SHE BE SO CRUEL TO US!

MEANWHILE, HER FRIEND WAS WORRIED.

SHE SITS ALONE, BROODING OVER THAT HEARTLESS MONK. IT IS NOT GOOD FOR HER HEALTH AND LOOKS. I MUST FIND SOMETHING TO DISTRACT HER.

A FEW DAYS LATER —

A FAMOUS SCULPTOR IS HOLDING AN EXHIBITION OF HIS WORKS. LET US GO AND SEE IT, VASAVADATTA.

ALL RIGHT, IF YOU INSIST.

AT THE SHOW, VASAVADATTA FORGOT HER SORROW FOR A WHILE.

SUCH EXQUISITE WORKMANSHIP!

WILL YOU SELL THIS TO ME?

YOU MIGHT FIND THE PRICE TOO HEAVY.

WHATEVER IT MAY COST, I AM PREPARED TO BUY IT. QUOTE YOUR PRICE.

IT'S YOURS, IF YOU AGREE TO DANCE AGAIN.

25

VASAVADATTA HESITATED —

TO...DANCE...

YOU CAN'T GO BACK ON YOUR WORD. YOU HAVE AGREED TO PAY WHATEVER PRICE HE ASKS.

VASAVADATTA RELUCTANTLY AGREED.

THE NEXT EVENING, PEOPLE FLOCKED TO THE TOWN HALL.

AT LAST WE WILL SEE VASAVADATTA DANCE AGAIN!

THANKS TO THE CHIEF SCULPTOR OF OUR CITY. IT WAS INDEED A CLEVER BARGAIN!

AT THE END OF THE PERFORMANCE, VASAVADATTA RECEIVED THUNDEROUS APPLAUSE. BUT INSTEAD OF MAKING HER HAPPY, IT ONLY MADE HER BROOD ALL THE MORE.

WHY DID THAT MONK SHUN ME WHEN THOUSANDS OF PEOPLE LONG FOR A SIGHT OF ME?

IN THE DAYS THAT FOLLOWED, THE CHIEF SCULPTOR BEGAN TO VISIT THE DANCER TO CAPTURE HER IMAGE IN STONE.

MY ART WILL DIE WITH ME. BUT YOURS WILL LAST FOR CENTURIES.

MY TALENT, WHICH BRINGS SO MUCH HAPPINESS TO YOU, ONLY MAKES MY ENVIOUS RIVALS HATE ME.

A FEW DAYS LATER, THE SCULPTOR SUDDENLY VANISHED.

WHY DOESN'T HE COME ? THE WORK IS YET TO BE COMPLETED. IT'S THREE DAYS SINCE HE LAST CAME !

PERHAPS HE IS OUT OF TOWN.

MEANWHILE, HIS FRIENDS AND RELATIVES TOO WERE SEARCHING FOR THE CHIEF SCULPTOR.

HAVE HIS RIVALS DONE AWAY WITH HIM ?

HE WAS LAST SEEN ENTERING THE HOUSE OF VASAVADATTA, THREE DAYS AGO.

LATER, THE BODY OF THE MISSING SCULPTOR WAS FOUND BURIED NOT FAR FROM VASAVADATTA'S HOUSE. SHE WAS CHARGED WITH THE MURDER OF THE SCULPTOR.

DO YOU HAVE ANYTHING TO SAY IN YOUR DEFENCE?

VASAVADATTA HAD NOTHING TO SAY.

VASAVADATTA IS GUILTY. CONFISCATE HER PROPERTY AND HAVE HER BANISHED FROM MATHURA.

AS VASAVADATTA WAS TURNED OUT OF HER HOUSE, AN ANGRY MOB JEERED AT HER AND PELTED HER WITH STONES.

TAKE THIS, YOU MURDERESS.

SEE THAT YOU NEVER DARKEN OUR CITY AGAIN!

BLEEDING PROFUSELY, VASAVADATTA REACHED THE OUTSKIRTS OF MATHURA AND FOUND REFUGE IN A CREMATORIUM.

VASAVADATTA, I KNOW YOU ARE INNOCENT! THEY HAVE DELIBERATELY DONE THIS TO YOU.

FRIEND, LET US NOT BLAME ANYONE.

PEOPLE COMING IN AND OUT OF MATHURA, LOOKED UPON VASAVADATTA, NOW SERIOUSLY ILL WITH FESTERING WOUNDS, AS AN UNTOUCHABLE.

SHE DOESN'T DESERVE ANY SYMPATHY.

LEAVE HER TO DIE. WHY DO YOU WASTE YOUR TIME ON HER?

THEY WOULD SPIT AT HER AND SOMETIMES EVEN STONE HER AS THEY PASSED BY.

THEN CAME UPAGUPTA, THE BUDDHIST MONK.

FRIEND, COVER MY BODY. LET HIM NOT SEE ME IN THIS STATE.

VASAVADATTA, I HAVE COME TO YOU.

O MONK, WHEN ALL MATHURA ADMIRED ME, YOU ALONE SPURNED ME.

WHY HAVE YOU CHOSEN TO VISIT ME NOW WHEN I AM A MASS OF FESTERING FLESH, SHUNNED BY ALL?

UPAGUPTA SMILED. AT THAT TIME YOU DID NOT NEED ME, VASAVADATTA. YOU DO, NOW. COME, LET US GO TO MY MONASTERY.

UPAGUPTA TOOK HER WITH HIM AND NURSED HER BACK TO HEALTH.

YOU SEEM SAD, VASAVA-DATTA.

I AM NO LONGER BEAUTIFUL.. NO ONE WILL LOOK AT ME NOW.

VASAVADATTA, YOU ARE YET TO DISCOVER A BEAUTY GREATER THAN THE ONE YOU HAVE LOST — THE BEAUTY OF THE SELF.

THE BEAUTY OF THE SELF?

CURIOUS TO KNOW MORE, SHE BEGAN TO ATTEND THE DISCOURSES OF LORD BUDDHA.

YOU CAN'T CALL EVEN THE BODY YOUR OWN. WHEN THE BODY IS CAST AWAY IT BECOMES FOOD FOR OTHERS. LIGHT THE LAMP WITHIN YOU, AND ONLY THEN WILL YOU FIND PEACE.

LIGHT THE LAMP WITHIN YOU ... PEACE ....

VASAVADATTA FELL AT THE FEET OF LORD BUDDHA.

LORD, ADMIT ME INTO YOUR ORDER.

SO BE IT, MY CHILD. MAY YOU FIND PEACE OF MIND.

Classic Collections

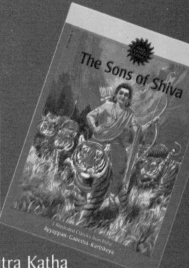

The immortal tales of Amar Chitra Katha
are now available as 3-in-1 digests with a special
selection of three delightful tales in one comic book.

Tales from the Panchatantra
Tales of Birbal
More Tales of Birbal
Great Plays of Kalidasa
Great Sanskrit Plays
Great Indian Emperors
Vishnu the Saviour
Ranas of Mewar

Matchless Wits
More Tales from the Jatakas
Vishnu to the Rescue
Buddhist Tales
More Buddhist Tales
Tales told by Sri Ramakrishna
Further Tales from the Jatakas
The Sons of the Pandavas

Each 96-page digest is now available at a special online price of
Rs 64 (MRP Rs 75) at www.AmarChitraKatha.com. Start your collection today!

INDIA BOOK HOUSE
Mahalaxmi Chambers, 5th Floor, 22 Bhulabhai Desai Road, Mumbai 400 026, India
Tel 23523827 Fax 23538406 Email info@amarchitrakatha.com

Buddha

Illustrated Classics From India

Buddha

Gautama Buddha was one of the most exceptional of free thinkers and religious leaders. Buddha was born as Prince Siddhartha to King Suddhodana and Queen Mayadevi in the Himalayan kingdom of Kapilavastu in 544 BC. Sage Asita visited the palace and predicted that the baby will live to be either the greatest of kings or the greatest of saints. Frightened by the prophecy, Suddhodana took great care to ensure that the young prince was surrounded only by beauty, luxury and happiness.

Years later, restless in his gilded cocoon, Siddhartha set out to explore his kingdom and was greatly moved at the state of human suffering. One fine day, he renounced the world and began a life of severe asceticism to seek an answer to life and sorrow, to seek the ultimate truth.

His search led him to enlightenment that liberated and illuminated him as he pondered under a Bodhi tree. He became the Buddha at the age of 35. He realised that the body need not suffer or starve to seek the truth. He adopted the "middle-path", that of moderation. He returned to preach what he had learnt and experienced, and did it with compassion for his fellow beings.

The noble Buddha then formed his first *sangha* and travelled through numerous lands for several years spreading his wisdom, reforming many kings and nobles and winning hundreds of followers. Buddha's gospel slowly spread further east, to the Asian countries, and became famous throughout the world. Today, the Buddha has followers across the world, but the largest numbers are concentrated in the South East Asian countries.

Script: S.K. Ramachandra   Illustrations: Souren Roy

IN THE HIMALAYAN FOOTHILLS, KAPILAVASTU WAS A SMALL BUT PROSPEROUS KINGDOM. THE SAKYAS RULED OVER IT. SUDDHODANA WAS THEIR KING.

ONE DAY, HIS QUEEN, MAYA-DEVI, DREAMT THAT A WHITE ELEPHANT WITH SIX TUSKS, PIERCED HER WOMB.

TEN MONTHS LATER THE QUEEN WAS ON HER WAY TO HER FATHER'S HOUSE. AS SHE WAS PASSING THROUGH A BEAUTIFUL GROVE ON THE WAY TO LUMBINI—

STOP! I WOULD LIKE TO SPEND SOME TIME HERE.

THE QUEEN GOT DOWN AND STARTED WALKING TOWARDS A SALA TREE IN THE MIDDLE OF THE GARDEN. SUDDENLY—

I AM IN GREAT PAIN. I MUST REST.

THERE A BABY WAS BORN TO HER. IT WAS THE FULL MOON NIGHT OF VAISAKHA. THERE WAS SILENCE ALL AROUND.

ON HEARING THE NEWS, THE KING RUSHED TO LUMBINI AND BROUGHT THE MOTHER AND THE CHILD TO THE PALACE. SAGE ASITA CAME TO THE PALACE TO SEE THE BABY.

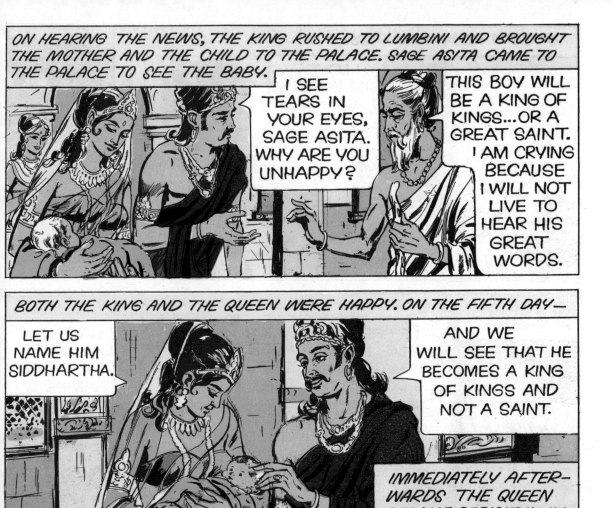

I SEE TEARS IN YOUR EYES, SAGE ASITA. WHY ARE YOU UNHAPPY?

THIS BOY WILL BE A KING OF KINGS...OR A GREAT SAINT. I AM CRYING BECAUSE I WILL NOT LIVE TO HEAR HIS GREAT WORDS.

BOTH THE KING AND THE QUEEN WERE HAPPY. ON THE FIFTH DAY—

LET US NAME HIM SIDDHARTHA.

AND WE WILL SEE THAT HE BECOMES A KING OF KINGS AND NOT A SAINT.

IMMEDIATELY AFTER-WARDS THE QUEEN BECAME SERIOUSLY ILL.

ON THE SEVENTH DAY AFTER THE BIRTH OF SIDDHARTHA—

SISTER PRAJAPATI, I SHALL SOON LEAVE THIS WORLD. WHEN I AM GONE, PLEASE BE A KIND MOTHER TO SIDDHARTHA. PROMISE ME.

I PROMISE.

AFTER A YEAR HAD PASSED—

YOU HAVE BEEN A GOOD MOTHER TO HIM, PRAJAPATI.

I LOVE HIM DEARLY. I AM PROUD TO BE HIS MOTHER.

AS SIDDHARTHA GREW, THE KING BECAME ANXIOUS ABOUT THE PROPHECY.

HE SPENDS SO MUCH TIME ALONE, UNDER THAT JAMBU TREE. I DON'T LIKE THAT.

HE SAYS, HIS PLAYMATES PLAY CRUEL GAMES.

ONE DAY AS SIDDHARTHA WAS WALKING ALONG IN THE GARDEN—

POOR BIRD! I WONDER WHOSE ARROW HAS HURT HIM.

SIDDHARTHA GENTLY REMOVED THE ARROW AND TENDED TO THE BIRD'S WOUND. SOME TIME LATER—

THIS IS MY BIRD. I SHOT IT! GIVE IT TO ME.

IT WAS DEVADATTA, SIDDHARTHA'S COUSIN.

DEVADATTA! IT IS SUCH A LOVELY BIRD. WHY DO YOU WISH TO HARM IT?

THE BIRD BELONGS TO ME. GIVE IT BACK.

I WON'T DO THAT.

THE MATTER WAS TAKEN TO THE COURT—

PRINCE! WHAT RIGHT HAVE YOU TO KEEP THE BIRD?

SIR, IF I HAD NOT REMOVED THE ARROW, THE BIRD WOULD HAVE DIED. THE BIRD OWES ITS LIFE TO ME. SHOULD THE BIRD BELONG TO THE ONE WHO TOOK ITS LIFE OR TO THE ONE WHO GAVE IT LIFE?

YEARS ROLLED BY. DANDAPANI, A SAKYAN NOBLE ARRANGED THE SWAYAMVARA OF HIS DAUGHTER, YASHODHARA. PRINCES FROM FAR AND NEAR CAME TO THE SWAYAMVARA.

YASHODHARA CHOSE SIDDHARTHA AS HER HUSBAND.

THE ASSEMBLED PRINCES WERE HURT BY YASHODHARA'S CHOICE. THEY APPROACHED DANDAPANI.

SIR THE PRINCESS SHOULD NOT BE MARRIED TO SIDDHARTHA. HE IS NOT A GOOD FIGHTER.

SIR, YOU SHOULD HOLD A TEST IN ARCHERY. THE PRINCESS SHOULD BE GIVEN IN MARRIAGE TO THE WINNER.

DANDAPANI TRIED TO PERSUADE HIS DAUGHTER.

YASHODHARA! CHOOSE SOME-ONE ELSE AS YOUR HUSBAND.

FATHER, I HAVE MADE MY CHOICE. PLEASE AGREE TO IT.

WHEN THE NEWS REACHED KING SUDDHODANA, HE FELT SAD.

FATHER, WHY ARE YOU SAD?

THE PEOPLE DON'T THINK YOU ARE A GOOD WARRIOR.

FATHER, LET DANDAPANI HOLD A TEST. I WILL TAKE PART IN IT.

I AM HAPPY TO HEAR THAT. YOUR ANCESTORS WERE GREAT WARRIORS, SIDDHARTHA.

MANY GATHERED TO WITNESS THE TEST.

IT IS SIDDHARTHA WHO HAS WON IN HORSE-RIDING.

NO ONE COULD EQUAL HIM IN ARCHERY TOO!

SIDDHARTHA AND YASHODHARA WERE MARRIED WITH GREAT POMP.

THE KING TRIED HIS BEST TO PROVIDE ALL THE COMFORTS OF LIFE TO SIDDHARTHA.

SOON, A SON WAS BORN TO THEM. KING SUDDHODANA WAS PLEASED WHEN HE HEARD THE NEWS.

LORD! IT IS A BOY!

GOOD! NOW SIDDHARTHA WILL NEVER THINK OF BECOMING A SAINT.

ONE DAY—

FATHER, I WOULD LIKE TO GO OUT OF THE PALACE AND SEE MORE OF THE WORLD.

I WILL ORDER A CHARIOT FOR YOU. AFTER IT IS READY, YOU CAN GO OUT IN IT.

A FEW DAYS LATER, IN A BEAUTIFUL CHARIOT WITH FOUR HORSES DRIVEN BY CHANNA, SIDDHARTHA DROVE THROUGH THE STREETS OF THE CITY.

HOW HANDSOME THE PRINCE IS.

I HAVE HEARD, HE IS BRAVE AND FEARLESS.

IN THE CITY, KING SUDDHODANA HAD ORDERED ALL SIGHTS OF UNHAPPINESS TO BE KEPT AWAY FROM SIDDHARTHA. BUT AS HE DROVE FURTHER—

HE IS AN OLD MAN, MASTER! HE IS BENT WITH AGE.

CHANNA, WHO IS THIS? HIS HEAD IS WHITE. HE SEEMS VERY WEAK. HIS SKIN IS WRINKLED.

DOES EVERYONE GET OLD, CHANNA?

YES, MY LORD! EVERYONE HAS TO GROW OLD.

WILL MY YASHODHARA ALSO GROW OLD? WILL MY STRENGTH GO AWAY WITH YEARS?

ON ANOTHER DAY—

WHAT IS THE MATTER WITH THIS MAN?

HE IS ILL, MY LORD! HE IS CRYING WITH PAIN.

IS DISEASE PECULIAR TO HIM?

NO, MY LORD! ANYONE MAY FALL ILL IN HIS LIFETIME.

10

EVEN I?

YES, MASTER, EVEN YOU.

STILL ANOTHER DAY—
WHY ARE THEY CARRYING THAT MAN, CHANNA?

HE IS DEAD, MY LORD!

IS HE THE ONLY DEAD MAN? OR DO OTHERS ALSO DIE?

EVERYONE WHO IS BORN, HAS TO DIE SOME DAY.

I FEEL SICK, CHANNA. LET US RETURN TO THE PALACE.

ON THE WAY BACK—

STOP, CHANNA! WHO IS THAT? HE LOOKS CALM AND DIFFERENT FROM ALL THE OTHER MEN I HAVE SEEN.

HE IS A SAINT. HE HAS GIVEN UP A LIFE OF PLEASURE AND PAIN IN SEARCH OF TRUTH.

AT THE PALACE—

SIDDHARTHA! PLEASE TELL ME THE CAUSE OF YOUR UNHAPPINESS!

MOTHER, I HAVE LEARNT THAT ALL THINGS ALIVE AND BEAUTIFUL KEEP CHANGING. MEN GROW OLD. MEN FALL ILL AND DIE. I FEEL UNHAPPY WHEN I THINK OF THESE THINGS.

IN THE MIDDLE OF THE NIGHT, HE MADE THE DECISION.

I MUST FIND A WAY TO END SORROW. I WILL GO IN SEARCH OF TRUTH, LIKE THAT SAINT.

CHANNA GET MY HORSE READY! I WISH TO RIDE OUT.

YES, MASTER!

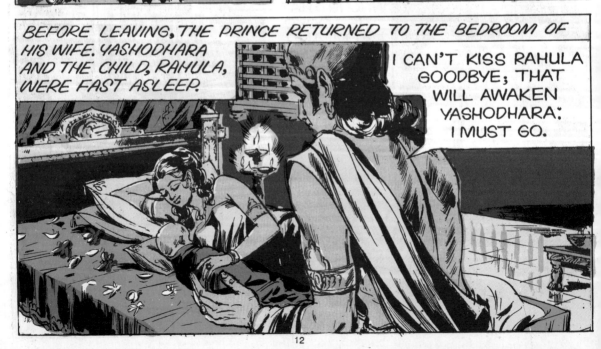

BEFORE LEAVING, THE PRINCE RETURNED TO THE BEDROOM OF HIS WIFE. YASHODHARA AND THE CHILD, RAHULA, WERE FAST ASLEEP.

I CAN'T KISS RAHULA GOODBYE; THAT WILL AWAKEN YASHODHARA: I MUST GO.

SIDDHARTHA MOUNTED HIS HORSE AND RODE OUT, ACCOMPANIED ONLY BY CHANNA.

ONCE THEY WERE OUTSIDE THE CITY, SIDDHARTHA GOT DOWN FROM THE HORSE.

CHANNA, TAKE ALL MY JEWELS AND RETURN TO KAPILAVASTU.

HE THEN CUT OFF HIS LONG HAIR AND WALKED ALONE.

LATER HE SAW A BEGGAR.

HALT, MY GOOD MAN! TAKE MY CLOTHES. AND GIVE ME YOURS.

WITH PLEASURE, MASTER.

SOON HE REACHED RAJAGRIHA, THE CAPITAL OF MAGADHA. HE WENT FROM HOUSE TO HOUSE SILENTLY WAITING TILL THE PEOPLE OFFERED HIM FOOD. KING BIMBISARA OBSERVED HIM FROM HIS PALACE.

LOOK AT THAT SAINT. HE LOOKS SO HANDSOME. FIND OUT WHO HE IS.

AS SOON AS THE MESSENGERS BROUGHT NEWS ABOUT SIDDHARTHA, KING BIMBISARA WENT TO MEET HIM.

YOU SEEM TO BE-LONG TO A NOBLE FAMILY. YOUR HAND SHOULD NOT HOLD A BEGGING BOWL, BUT THE REINS OF AN EMPIRE. I WILL GIVE YOU A HIGH POSITION IN MY KINGDOM. COME.

O KING, YOU ARE KIND. BUT I CANNOT ACCEPT YOUR INVITATION. I FEEL THAT LIFE IS FULL OF SORROW. I WISH TO FIND A WAY TO END ALL SORROW.

IF THAT IS YOUR WISH, I PRAY THAT YOU FIND IT. PLEASE COME AND TEACH ME WHEN YOU HAVE FOUND THE SOLUTION.

FROM RAJAGRIHA, SIDDHARTHA WENT IN SEARCH OF THE GREAT SAGES OF THOSE DAYS. NOT SATISFIED WITH THEIR TEACHINGS, HE ENTERED THE THICK JUNGLES OF URUBILVA, NEAR GAYA OF TODAY.

THERE WERE FIVE HERMITS IN THE JUNGLES OF URUBILVA.

THIS MAN IS KEEN ON HIS GOAL. HE IS SURE TO SUCCEED. LET US WAIT ON HIM.

SIDDHARTHA DRANK ONLY WATER AND ATE ONLY FRUITS AND HERBS. HE SLEPT ON THE HARD GROUND. AFTER SOME TIME HE STARTED EATING ONLY ONE HEMP GRAIN EVERY DAY. THIS MADE HIM VERY WEAK. ONE DAY, WHEN HE HAD GONE TO BATHE IN THE RIVER-

I FEEL WEAK. I DON'T HAVE STRENGTH TO GET UP.

HE CAUGHT HOLD OF A LOW BRANCH OF A TREE AND RAISED HIMSELF WITH ITS SUPPORT.

BUT AS HE BEGAN TO WALK AWAY FROM THE BANK, HE FELT WEAK AND FELL DOWN.

SLOWLY HE GOT UP.

NEXT DAY, AS HE SAT BENEATH A BANIAN TREE, SUJATA, DAUGHTER OF A HERDSMAN, CAME TO THAT SPOT. SHE OFFERED FOOD TO BUDDHA.

THANK YOU FOR FEEDING ME.

LATER—

HOW IS IT THAT YOU HAVE STARTED EATING FOOD AGAIN?

I HAVE COME TO BELIEVE THAT STARVING DOES NOT HELP IN REACHING THE TRUTH.

THE FIVE ASCETICS WERE DISAPPOINTED.

HE DOES NOT DESERVE OUR RESPECT.

YES, HE WANTS THE PLEASURES OF LIFE.

16

SIDDHARTHA NOW LIVED A LONELY LIFE.

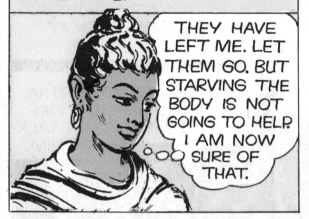

THEY HAVE LEFT ME. LET THEM GO. BUT STARVING THE BODY IS NOT GOING TO HELP. I AM NOW SURE OF THAT.

HE MOVED TOWARDS A BODHI TREE AND SAT BENEATH IT.

HEAT AND COLD, HUNGER AND THIRST TROUBLED HIM. RAIN LASHED ON HIM.

COME WHAT MAY, I SHALL NOT MOVE FROM THIS SEAT TILL I FIND A WAY TO END SORROW.

VISIONS OF THE LIFE OF PLEASURE FLOATED BEFORE HIS EYES. BUT NOTHING COULD TEMPT HIM.

AND THEN HE SAW LIGHT.

SIDDHARTHA BECAME THE BUDDHA, THE ENLIGHTENED ONE.

I KNOW. I KNOW THE TRUTH NOW. THE WAY TO END SORROW IS FOUND.

HE SPENT SEVEN WEEKS UNDER THE TREE ENJOYING HIS STATE OF PERFECT HAPPINESS. THEN HE WENT OUT INTO THE WORLD TO TEACH OTHERS. FIRST, HE WENT TO BANARAS, IN SEARCH OF THE FIVE ASCETICS, WHO WERE WITH HIM IN URUBILVA. HE FOUND THEM IN DEER PARK.

HERE COMES SIDDHARTHA. HE RETURNED TO A LIFE OF EASE. LET US NOT TALK TO HIM.

BUT AS SOON AS HE CAME NEAR, THEY GOT UP AND RECEIVED HIM WITH RESPECT.

I HAVE COME TO TELL YOU WHAT I HAVE FOUND. LISTEN!

WHEN THEY HEARD THE BUDDHA, THEY BECAME HIS DISCIPLES. THE SANGHA THUS CAME INTO BEING.

THERE IS GREAT SORROW IN THIS WORLD. THIS SORROW IS BECAUSE OF DESIRE. IF YOU CAN FREE YOURSELF FROM DESIRE, YOU WILL BE FREE FROM SORROW. I WILL SHOW YOU THE WAY TO REMOVE SORROW FROM THE MIND.

AFTER THAT, HE RETURNED TO URUBILVA AND WENT TO THE HOUSE OF KASSHYAPA, A GREAT BRAHMAN.

WHAT DO YOU WANT?

I WANT TO SPEND A NIGHT HERE.

YOU ARE WELCOME. PLEASE COME IN.

KASSHYAPA WAS A WORSHIPPER OF AGNI, THE GOD OF FIRE.

MAY I STAY IN THE ROOM, WHERE YOU KEEP THE SACRED FIRE?

HAVEN'T YOU HEARD THAT THE SACRED FIRE IS GUARDED BY A SERPENT AT NIGHT? THE SERPENT WILL BITE YOU IF YOU GO NEAR THE FIRE.

I AM NOT AFRAID. PLEASE ALLOW ME TO SPEND THE NIGHT THERE.

AT LAST KASSHYAPA AGREED. BUDDHA SAT SILENTLY BEFORE THE FIRE. KASSHYAPA WENT TO SLEEP OUTSIDE.

EARLY NEXT MORNING –

LET ME GO AND LOOK FOR HIM. HE MUST BE DEAD. POOR MAN!

WHEN HE WENT INSIDE THE ROOM, HE SAW BUDDHA SITTING PEACEFULLY. THE LIGHT FROM THE FIRE SHONE ON HIS FACE.

I ACCEPT YOU AS MY MASTER. TEACH ME.

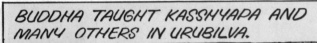

BUDDHA TAUGHT KASSHYAPA AND MANY OTHERS IN URUBILVA.

ONE DAY— MASTER, I HAVE HEARD THAT KING BIMBISARA WILL BE CELEBRATING A GREAT YAGNA.

LET US GO TO RAJAGRIHA.

ON THEIR WAY TO RAJAGRIHA, THEY SAW A HERD OF SHEEP. THERE WAS A LAME LAMB. BUDDHA LIFTED IT IN HIS ARMS.

POOR THING, IT MUST HAVE BEEN SUFFERING A LOT OF PAIN.

GOOD MAN, WHERE ARE YOU GOING?

I AM GOING TO RAJA-GRIHA. THESE SHEEP BELONG TO THE KING. THEY ARE GOING TO BE SACRIFICED IN THE YAGNA – IN THE SACRED FIRE.

BIMBISARA HEARD THAT BUDDHA WAS ON HIS WAY TO RAJAGRIHA, HE WENT FORWARD WITH HIS MINISTERS TO MEET HIM.

HE IS IN THE COMPANY OF URUBILVA KASSHYAPA. DOES THAT MEAN BUDDHA IS HIS DISCIPLE?

WHEN THEY CAME NEAR, BUDDHA GENTLY PLACED THE LAMB DOWN.

YOU HAD EXPRESSED THE WISH TO SEE ME AFTER I HAD FOUND THE WAY. HERE I AM.

HOLY ONE! I AM ABOUT TO BEGIN A YAGNA. GREAT KASSHYAPA AND YOU ARE ALSO WELCOME TO TAKE PART IN IT.

O KING, KILLING OF INNOCENT ANIMALS CANNOT BE A GOOD DEED. THE WAY TO HAPPINESS DOES NOT LIE IN YAGNA.

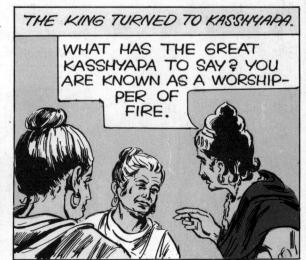

THE KING TURNED TO KASSHYAPA.

WHAT HAS THE GREAT KASSHYAPA TO SAY? YOU ARE KNOWN AS A WORSHIPPER OF FIRE.

KASSHYAPA BOWED TO BUDDHA.

I AM A DISCIPLE OF BUDDHA.

I SEE. BUDDHA IS THE TEACHER. DON'T YOU ALSO BELIEVE IN YAGNA?

BUDDHA HAS SHOWN ME THE RIGHT WAY. NEITHER THE WORSHIP OF FIRE NOR THE SACRIFICE OF DUMB ANIMALS CAN MAKE US FREE FROM SORROW.

THE KING TURNED TO BUDDHA.

MASTER, LET US HEAR YOUR WORDS OF WISDOM.

AND BUDDHA TAUGHT THEM.

LORD, I HAVE GIVEN UP THE IDEA OF PERFORMING YAGNA. I TAKE REFUGE IN BUDDHA.

NEXT DAY, THE KING INVITED BUDDHA AND HIS DISCIPLES FOR A MEAL AT HIS PALACE. AFTER THE MEAL WAS OVER —

LORD, I GIVE VENUVANA, MY GARDEN AS A GIFT TO THE SANGHA. PLEASE ACCEPT IT.

ONE DAY, KRISHA GOTAMI BROUGHT BEFORE BUDDHA HER DEAD CHILD.

MASTER, PLEASE BRING IT BACK TO LIFE. IT IS MY ONLY CHILD.

CONTROL YOUR GRIEF. DO AS I SAY. GET ME A FEW MUSTARD SEEDS FROM ANY HOUSE, WHERE NO DEATH HAS TAKEN PLACE. AND I WILL BRING BACK TO LIFE YOUR CHILD.

FROM HOUSE TO HOUSE KRISHA GOTAMI WENT.

I LOST MY HUSBAND LAST YEAR!

I LOST MY TWO CHILDREN.

MY MOTHER DIED YESTERDAY.

DISAPPOINTED KRISHA GOTAMI CAME BACK TO BUDDHA.

LORD! I COULD NOT FIND A PLACE WHERE NO DEATH HAS OCCURRED.

MY CHILD ALL THAT IS BORN, MUST DIE ONE DAY. THERE IS ULTIMATELY NOTHING BUT SORROW IN LIFE. IT IS FREEDOM FROM DESIRE THAT FREES US FROM SORROW.

AFTER A FEW YEARS, AT SUDDHODANA'S COURT_

LORD! OUR PRINCE HAS BECOME FAMOUS. MANY HAVE BECOME HIS DISCIPLES. THEY ARE SPREADING HIS TEACHINGS.

GO TO SIDDHARTHA AND TELL HIM THAT I AM GROWING OLD AND WISH TO SEE HIM BEFORE I DIE.

WHEN BUDDHA REACHED KAPILAVASTU_

WELCOME MY SON! I WISH YOU WOULD BECOME KING.

I AM SORRY. I HAVE CHOSEN THE PATH OF PEACE.

THE KING ARRANGED FOR BUDDHA'S STAY IN A GROVE NEARBY.

NEXT MORNING—

LORD, THE PRINCE IS GOING FROM HOUSE TO HOUSE TO RECEIVE ALMS IN THE CITY!!

QUICK. LEAD ME TO HIM.

MY SON, MUST YOU BEG?

BUT IT IS OUR CUSTOM.

WHAT DO YOU MEAN? YOU ARE DESCENDED FROM KINGS.

O GREAT KING, YOU CLAIM DESCENT FROM KINGS. MY DESCENT IS FROM THE BUDDHAS OF OLD. THEY ALWAYS BEGGED FOR THEIR FOOD AND LIVED ON ALMS.

ONCE THEY REACHED THE PALACE, BUDDHA SPOKE SOFTLY TO ALL THOSE THAT HAD GATHERED.

HIS WORDS ARE THE WORDS OF A GREAT MAN.

THEY BRING PEACE TO THE HEART.

BUDDHA NOTICED THAT YASHODHARA WAS NOT PRESENT.

WHERE IS YASHODHARA?

SHE HAS REFUSED TO COME.

SHE HAS BEEN VERY UN-HAPPY EVER SINCE YOU LEFT. SHE HAS CUT HER HAIR, WEARS SIMPLE CLOTHES AND EATS SPARINGLY JUST AS YOU DID.

WITH TWO OF HIS DISCIPLES, BUDDHA WENT TO YASHODHARA'S CHAMBER.

I MUST TRY TO HEAL THE SORROW IN HER HEART.

WHEN YASHODHARA SAW BUDDHA, SHE FELL AT HIS FEET AND WEPT.

THEN REMEMBERING THAT OTHERS WERE PRESENT, SHE GOT UP AND SAT AT A LITTLE DISTANCE.

BUDDHA SPOKE WORDS OF COMFORT.

A WEEK AFTER · BUDDHA CAME TO KAPILAVASTU.

RAHULA, DO YOU SEE THE MAN SITTING THERE IN THE CENTRE? HE IS YOUR FATHER. GO TO HIM AND ASK FOR YOUR SHARE OF HIS PROPERTY.

RAHULA WENT TO BUDDHA.

FATHER! MY MOTHER SENT ME TO ASK YOU FOR MY SHARE OF YOUR PROPERTY.

BUDDHA TURNED TO SARI-PUTRA, HIS DISCIPLE.

MY SON ASKS FOR HIS INHERITANCE. WELL THEN, TAKE HIM IN THE SANGHA.

AFTER RAHULA JOINED THE SANGHA, MANY YOUNG MEN OF THE ROYAL FAMILY ALSO JOINED. AMONGST THEM WAS DEVADATTA. HE ALSO MOVED ABOUT WITH BUDDHA. ONE DAY—

MASTER, YOU SHOULD REST. I SHALL LEAD THE SANGHA.

NO, DEVA-DATTA THE SANGHA STILL NEEDS MY GUIDANCE.

DEVADATTA FELT JEALOUS OF BUDDHA. HE WENT TO RAJAGRIHA AND MET AJATASATRU, SON OF KING BIMBISARA.

PRINCE AJATASATRU! HOW LONG CAN YOU WAIT TO BECOME A KING? PUT YOUR FATHER IN PRISON AND BE A KING YOURSELF.

IT IS A GOOD IDEA, DEVADATTA. I WILL DO AS YOU SAY.

AJATASATRU DID AS DEVA-DATTA ADVISED HIM.

IT IS NICE TO BE A KING. THANK YOU, DEVADATTA! IF YOU WANT MY HELP IN ANYTHING, ASK FOR IT.

I NEED YOUR HELP, KING AJATASATRU. HELP ME KILL BUDDHA. I HATE HIM.

DEVADATTA TRIED MANY WAYS TO KILL BUDDHA.

LOOK OUT! A BIG STONE IS ROLLING DOWN TOWARDS BUDDHA.

SIT WHERE YOU ARE. NO HARM WILL COME TO ME.

THE ROCK SPLIT INTO TWO AND A PIECE FELL ON EITHER SIDE OF BUDDHA.

MANY OF DEVADATTA'S FOLLOWERS CAME TO JOIN THE SANGHA OF BUDDHA.

THE ROCK DID NOT KILL HIM.

HE LOOKS FRAIL, BUT HE IS GREAT. LET US GO TO HIM.

I HEAR, MANY OF MY FOLLOWERS HAVE JOINED HIS SANGHA. WHY NOT SET AN ELEPHANT ON HIM?

YET ANOTHER ORDER FROM AJATASATRU.

INTOXICATE THE ELEPHANT NALAGIRI, AND THEN LET HIM LOOSE IN THE PATH OF BUDDHA.

RUN, RUN, NALAGIRI IS FREE. HE HAS RUINED HALF THE TOWN ALREADY. TWENTY MEN HAVE BEEN KILLED.

MASTER, LET US HIDE. A WILD ELEPHANT IS COMING THIS WAY.

NO, HE WON'T HARM US.

NALAGIRI CAME THUMPING ALONG AND RUSHED TOWARDS BUDDHA IN A MAD FURY.

BUDDHA SMILED AND RAISED HIS HAND. THE ELEPHANT, AT ONCE CALMED, KNELT AT HIS FEET.

AJATASATRU WAS AN UNHAPPY MAN. HE FELL ILL OFTEN. JIVAKA WAS HIS PHYSICIAN.

JIVAKA, WHY DO I SUFFER?

YOUR AILMENT IS NOT PHYSICAL BUT SPIRITUAL. ONLY BUDDHA CAN HELP YOU.

LET US GO TO HIM, THEN. WHERE WILL HE BE NOW?

IN THE AMRAVANA, AT VAISHALI..

.WHICH BELONGS TO AMRAPALI, THE COURTESAN?

YES, MY LORD! AMRAPALI HAS GIFTED IT TO BUDDHA.

WHEN AJATASATRU REACHED AMRAVANA—

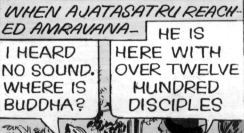

I HEARD NO SOUND. WHERE IS BUDDHA?

HE IS HERE WITH OVER TWELVE HUNDRED DISCIPLES

AJATASATRU'S MIND TROUBLED HIM.

TWELVE HUNDRED PEOPLE! NOT A SOUND OF HUMAN HABITATION HERE!! HAVE YOU BROUGHT ME HERE TO BE KILLED? IS IT A PLOT OF YOURS?

MY LORD! TRUST ME. LET US GO AHEAD.

AND AJATASATRU WAS SPELL-BOUND WHEN HE SAW THE ASSEMBLY OF MEN LISTENING QUIETLY TO THE GREAT TEACHER.

ALL SUFFERING AND PAIN, FEAR AND HATRED, COME FROM DESIRE. THE MAN WHO IS FREE FROM ALL DESIRE, NEED NOT WORRY. WHOM HAS HE TO FEAR?

HOW SOOTHING!

AJATASATRU BECAME A DISCIPLE OF BUDDHA.

NOT MUCH LATER, DEVADATTA ALSO REPENTED. ONE DAY, HE SAID TO HIS FOLLOWERS—

CHILDREN, TAKE ME TO BUDDHA. HE ALONE CAN BRING PEACE TO MY TROUBLED MIND.

31

THE MEN CARRYING DEVADATTA KEPT DOWN THE LITTER AND WENT TO REFRESH THEMSELVES.

WHERE HAVE MY MEN GONE? I AM IN A HURRY TO MEET BUDDHA.

BEFORE HE COULD REACH BUDDHA, HE TOTTERED AND FELL.

I AM DYING, BUT NOW I KNOW THAT BUDDHA IS INDEED THE ENLIGHTENED ONE – THE TEACHER OF ALL. I TAKE REFUGE IN HIM.

BUDDHAM SARANAM GACCHAMI

SANGHAM SARANAM GACCHAMI

DHAMMAM SARANAM GACCHAMI

BUDDHA LIVED TO A RIPE OLD AGE. MILLIONS TOOK REFUGE IN HIM AND IN HIS TEACHINGS. PEOPLE, WHO SPOKE DIFFERENT LANGUAGES AND BELONGED TO DISTANT LANDS BECAME HIS FOLLOWERS.

Angulimala
The Robber who became a Saint

AMAR CHITRA KATHA

Illustrated Classics From India

Angulimala

Having realised the cause of human suffering and the remedy thereof, Lord Buddha wandered from place to place to enlighten the people. His teachings concern the forces that cause bondage and the means by which salvation can be achieved. He was received with great respect wherever he went.

Prasenajit, the King of Kosala, who ruled from his capital Shravasti, was a great admirer of Lord Buddha, although he had not converted to Buddhism. In the forest on the outskirts of Shravasti lived Angulimala, the dreaded highway robber who plundered and killed travelling traders. Fearing him, people eventually gave up travelling by the road that passed though his haunts. Though everybody shunned Angulimala, Buddha chose to cross his path. In the encounter between the forces of non-violence and violence, the former prevailed and Angulimala became a disciple of Lord Buddha.

The story Angulimala is taken from the Buddhist text *Paramatthadipani* of Dhammapala. This famous story of the saint and the sinner tells of the angst of the murderous dacoit Angulimala as opposed to the meditative calm of Lord Buddha, and the subsequent spiritual emancipation of Angulimala.

Script: Subba Rao Illustrations: Pratap Mulick

ANGULIMALA

LONG, LONG AGO, A KING CALLED PRASENAJIT RULED OVER KOSALA* FROM HIS CAPITAL, SHRAVASTI. ONE NIGHT WHEN HE WAS FAST ASLEEP...

...THE ROOM WAS SUDDENLY LIT BY FLASHES OF LIGHT. HE WOKE UP WITH A START.

WHO—WHAT'S THAT? THE WEAPONS! WHAT'S HAPPENING TO THEM? WHY DO THEY GLITTER SO?

* PART OF MODERN U.P.

THE NEXT MOMENT HOWEVER ALL WAS DARK AGAIN.

WAS IT A NIGHTMARE? WAS MY IMAGINATION PLAYING TRICKS ON ME? OR WAS I REALLY DAZZLED BY THE LIGHT FROM THE WEAPONS?

THE NEXT MORNING, ANY DOUBTS HE MIGHT HAVE HAD, VANISHED.

AT MIDNIGHT, THE WEAPONS IN THE ARMOURY AND IN EVERY HOUSE OF KOSALA, BLAZED, FOR A MOMENT, WITH A BRILLIANT LIGHT.

A STRANGE THING HAPPENED LAST NIGHT, YOUR MAJESTY!

AT THAT MOMENT, IN THE HOUSE OF THE ROYAL PRIEST, GARGA —

HOW HANDSOME IS OUR NEW-BORN SON!

HE IS, NO DOUBT. BUT I AM WORRIED. IMMEDIATELY AFTER HIS BIRTH, STRANGE LIGHTS ISSUED FORTH FROM THE WEAPONS OF THE NIGHT-GUARDS.

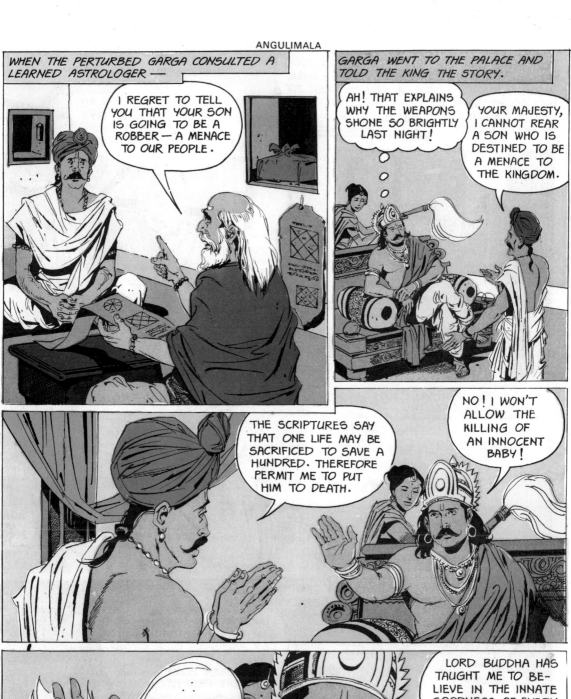

WHEN THE PERTURBED GARGA CONSULTED A LEARNED ASTROLOGER —

I REGRET TO TELL YOU THAT YOUR SON IS GOING TO BE A ROBBER — A MENACE TO OUR PEOPLE.

GARGA WENT TO THE PALACE AND TOLD THE KING THE STORY.

AH! THAT EXPLAINS WHY THE WEAPONS SHONE SO BRIGHTLY LAST NIGHT!

YOUR MAJESTY, I CANNOT REAR A SON WHO IS DESTINED TO BE A MENACE TO THE KINGDOM.

THE SCRIPTURES SAY THAT ONE LIFE MAY BE SACRIFICED TO SAVE A HUNDRED. THEREFORE PERMIT ME TO PUT HIM TO DEATH.

NO! I WON'T ALLOW THE KILLING OF AN INNOCENT BABY!

LORD BUDDHA HAS TAUGHT ME TO BELIEVE IN THE INNATE GOODNESS OF EVERY LIVING CREATURE.

LET YOUR SON HAVE A SOUND EDUCATION. UNDER YOUR GUIDANCE, I HAVE NO DOUBT THAT HE WILL GROW UP TO BE A GOOD CITIZEN.

THANK YOU, YOUR MAJESTY. I WILL TRY MY BEST TO INSTIL VIRTUE IN HIM.

THE INFANT WHO WAS NAMED AHIMSAKA, GREW UP TO BE AN INTELLIGENT BOY.

ONE AS DEDICATED AS HE IS TO THE STUDY OF THE SCRIPTURES, CAN NEVER BECOME A ROBBER.

THEN, WHEN AHIMSAKA WAS ABOUT FOURTEEN YEARS OLD—

FATHER, PLEASE, PERMIT ME TO GO TO TAKSHASHILA*.

YOU MAY GO, MY SON. YOU HAVE MY BLESSINGS.

AHIMSAKA LEFT FOR TAKSHASHILA THAT VERY DAY.

ALL THE WAY TO TAKSHASHILA FOR THE SAKE OF LEARNING! HOW CAN AHIMSAKA EVER BECOME A ROBBER? THERE MUST HAVE BEEN SOME MISTAKE IN THE PROPHECY.

* A RENOWNED CENTRE OF LEARNING

ON REACHING TAKSHASHILA, AHIMSAKA WENT TO A GREAT SCHOLAR OF THOSE DAYS.

I, AHIMSAKA, SON OF GARGA OF SHRAVASTI, SALUTE YOU. ACCEPT ME AS YOUR DISCIPLE, MASTER.

YOU ARE WELCOME, MY SON. I WILL TEACH YOU.

AHIMSAKA SOON WON THE HEART OF THE MASTER.

LOOK AT AHIMSAKA. WITHIN SUCH A SHORT TIME, HE HAS MASTERED WHAT YOU COULD NOT IN THE LAST THREE YEARS. HE HAS A GREAT FUTURE BEFORE HIM.

SUCH COMMENTS AROUSED THE JEALOUSY OF THE OTHER DISCIPLES.

AHIMSAKA THINKS TOO MUCH OF HIMSELF.

OUR TEACHER'S PRAISE HAS GONE TO HIS HEAD.

WE MUST DO SOMETHING ABOUT IT.

THEY HATCHED A PLOT TO ESTRANGE THE MASTER FROM HIS FAVOURITE DISCIPLE.

QUICK! THE MASTER IS APPROACH- ING. LET US BEGIN OUR LITTLE DRAMA.

AHIMSAKA IS A GREAT SCHOLAR.

THAT'S WHY OUR MASTER PRAISES HIM SO.

INDEED, HE IS A GREATER SCHOLAR EVEN THAN OUR MASTER.

AT LEAST THE WIFE OF OUR REVERED MASTER THINKS SO.

THE MASTER BECAME THOUGHTFUL.

PERHAPS THERE IS AN ELEMENT OF TRUTH IN WHAT THE BOYS SAY.

ONE DAY AHIMSAKA MAY PROVE TO BE MORE LEARNED THAN ME. I MUST SEE THAT HE IS MADE AN OUT-CASTE, SHUNNED BY ALL.

WHEN HE ENTERED THE HOUSE —

DOES MY WIFE REALLY THINK HE IS A GREATER SCHOLAR THAN ME? HOW ATTENTIVELY SHE LISTENS TO WHAT HE SAYS! DOES SHE HAVE A GREATER REGARD FOR HIM THAN SHE HAS FOR ME?

WHATEVER THE TRUTH MAY BE, AHIMSAKA WILL HAVE TO GO.

HE ENTERED THE HALL STEALTHILY SO THAT HIS WIFE AND AHIMSAKA, DEEPLY ENGROSSED IN THEIR DISCUSSIONS, WOULD NOT NOTICE HIS PRESENCE.

AHIMSAKA!
GET UP!

I HAVE BEEN STANDING HERE ALL THIS WHILE. HAVE YOU BECOME SO ARROGANT THAT YOU FORGET TO ACKNOWLEDGE THE PRESENCE OF YOUR GURU *?

PARDON ME, MASTER. I...

THE MASTER, HOWEVER, DIDN'T GIVE HIM A CHANCE TO CONTINUE.

HUMILITY SHOULD BE THE OUTCOME OF KNOWLEDGE, NOT ARROGANCE. YOU HAVE NO PLACE HERE. YOU MAY GO.

AS A BEMUSED AHIMSAKA WALKED AWAY FROM THE MASTER'S HOUSE, THE OTHER DISCIPLES GLOATED OVER THE SUCCESS OF THEIR PLOT.

IT WORKED!

I WAS CERTAIN IT WOULD.

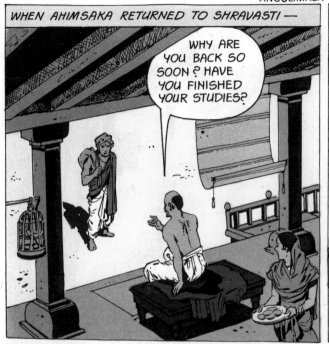

WHEN AHIMSAKA RETURNED TO SHRAVASTI —

WHY ARE YOU BACK SO SOON? HAVE YOU FINISHED YOUR STUDIES?

NO, FATHER. I WAS SENT AWAY. I INCURRED THE DISPLEASURE OF MY MASTER. BUT I...

WHAT! INCURRED THE DISPLEASURE OF YOUR MASTER! DON'T SHOW ME YOUR ACCURSED FACE! GO AWAY FROM HERE!

WHAT HAVE I DONE TO DESERVE SUCH A FATE? WHAT SHALL I DO?

I WILL TRY TO MAKE A LIVING WITH WHAT LITTLE KNOWLEDGE I HAVE.

BUT AHIMSAKA'S EFFORTS TO FIND SOME WORK PROVED FUTILE.

EMPLOY A YOUTH WHO HAS INCURRED THE DISPLEASURE OF HIS MASTER? NEVER!

HE WAS SHUNNED BY ALL.

AHIMSAKA IS COMING THIS WAY.

CLOSE THE DOOR! I DON'T WANT HIM TO ENTER OUR HOUSE AND POLLUTE IT.

THEY SLAM THEIR DOORS ON MY FACE. WHY MY MASTER SENT ME AWAY, I STILL DO NOT KNOW. FATHER DID NOT EVEN WANT TO HEAR MY STORY.

DEEP IN THOUGHT, AHIMSAKA LEFT KOSALA.

WHAT WAS MY FAULT? WHY HAVE I BEEN TREATED SO CRUELLY? THEY LABEL ME A SINNER. BUT IT IS I WHO HAVE BEEN SINNED AGAINST.

SUDDENLY —

SURRENDER WHATEVER YOU HAVE IF YOU VALUE YOUR LIFE.

NO! NO! NO!

TAKE THIS! AND THIS! THERE! I AM GIVING YOU ALL THAT I HAVE!

MERCY! PLEASE HAVE MERCY ON ME.

DISGUSTED, AHIMSAKA LET HIM GO.

HE HAS SHOWN ME THE WAY. I WILL BE A HIGHWAY ROBBER. I'LL BE MAKING A LIVING WHILE I TAKE REVENGE ON THE SOCIETY THAT REJECTED ME.

LATER, IN THE EVENING, A FLEET OF BULLOCK CARTS CARRYING MERCHANDISE PASSED THAT WAY ON THEIR WAY TO KAUSHAMBI.

HALT!

MY GOD! A ROBBER!

* LITTLE FINGERS

SOON, AHIMSAKA'S ATROCIOUS DEEDS BECAME THE TALK OF KOSALA.

HE IS A MONSTER.

WHO IS HE?

NO ONE KNOWS WHO HE IS NOR WHERE HE COMES FROM.

HE WEARS A STRANGE GARLAND...

SO I'VE HEARD—AN ANGULIMALA!*

AND AHIMSAKA BEGAN TO BE KNOWN AS ANGULIMALA.

THE TRADERS WHO HAD TO TRAVEL, CARRYING MERCHANDISE, WERE THE WORST HIT BY ANGULIMALA, AS THE SHORTEST ROUTE TO KAUSHAMBI WAS THROUGH ANGULIMALA'S HAUNTS.

STOP!

IT'S ANGULIMALA! DRIVE FASTER.

HA, HA! THERE IS NO ESCAPE FROM ME. GET DOWN ALL OF YOU.

*A GARLAND OF LITTLE FINGERS

AS SOON AS THE MERCHANTS WERE MASSACRED BY ANGULIMALA—

COME, MY FRIENDS! THIS FEAST IS FOR YOU.

AHA! HOW DID YOU ESCAPE MY SWORD?

SPARE MY LIFE. HAVE MERCY ON ME.

MERCY? WHAT DOES THAT MEAN?

I WANT TO LIVE FOR THE SAKE OF MY LITTLE SON...

AND I WANT TO KILL YOU FOR YOUR LITTLE FINGER; HA! HA!

AT LAST THE TERROR-STRICKEN SUBJECTS TURNED TO PRASENAJIT.

YOUR MAJESTY, DELIVER US FROM ANGULI-MALA.

I WILL COMMAND MY FOREST GUARDS TO CAPTURE THE NOTORIOUS MURDERER.

AS THE FOREST GUARDS ENTERED ANGULIMALA'S HAUNT —

A WHOLE ARMY OF THEM! GOOD! THAT MANY MORE FINGERS FOR MY GARLAND!

LIFTING UP HUGE BOULDERS, ANGULIMALA HURLED THEM AT THE GUARDS...

...AND THEN SPRANG UPON THEM.

A FEW, HOWEVER, WERE ABLE TO ESCAPE WITH THEIR LIVES.

16

WHEN THEY REPORTED TO PRASENAJIT—

JUST ONE MAN, AND YOU WERE HELPLESS AGAINST HIM!

THAT EVENING, THE ROYAL DRUMMER WENT ROUND THE CITY.

GIVE EAR! GIVE EAR! PEOPLE ARE ADVISED TO AVOID ANGULIMALA. THOSE GOING TO KAUSHAMBI SHOULD TAKE THE ROUTE VIA MAGADHA...

ANGULIMALA WAITED IN VAIN FOR VICTIMS.

MY GARLAND HAS BEGUN TO WITHER. I NEED NEW FINGERS! I WISH SOMEONE WOULD PASS THIS WAY.

SUDDENLY HE SPOTTED A MONK WALKING BY.

MY PRAYER HAS BEEN HEARD!

HALT!

ANGULIMALA RAN AFTER THE MONK.

TO HIS ASTONISHMENT, HOWEVER, THE MONK, WHO SEEMED TO BE WALKING AT A LEISURELY PACE, WAS ALWAYS A STEP AHEAD.

AT LAST EXHAUSTED BY THE CHASE, ANGULIMALA PAUSED.

O MONK, STOP! STOP MOVING.

I AM NOT MOVING. I AM AT REST. IT IS YOU WHO ARE IN PERPETUAL MOTION.

ANGULIMALA COLLAPSED AT THE FEET OF THE MONK.

GET UP, MY CHILD.

MASTER!

MASTER, HENCEFORTH I WILL NEVER KILL.

THE MONK BROUGHT HIM TO THE MONASTERY ON THE OUTSKIRTS OF SHRAVASTI.

SALUTATIONS TO YOU, MY MASTER.

ANATHAPINDIKA, I HAVE BROUGHT YET ANOTHER BROTHER—ANGULIMALA.

THE LOVING MONK WAS NONE OTHER THAN LORD BUDDHA.

THE NEXT MORNING, PRASENAJIT VISITED THE MONASTERY. THE KING HAD COME TO PAY HIS RESPECTS TO THE MASTER.

IT LOOKS AS THOUGH YOU HAVE STARTED ON AN EXPEDITION.

YES, MASTER. I WANT TO EXTERMINATE THAT MONSTER—ANGULIMALA. I HAVE COME FOR YOUR BLESSINGS.

SUPPOSING ANGULIMALA GIVES UP THE PATH OF VIOLENCE AND BEGINS TO LIVE THE LIFE OF AN ASCETIC, WHAT WILL YOUR REACTION BE?

I WILL SALUTE HIM THEN, MY LORD. BUT PARDON ME, I CAN'T IMAGINE ANGULIMALA AS AN ASCETIC.

BUT HE HAS BECOME ONE. THERE HE IS, WATERING THE PLANTS.

WHAT!

21

I COULD NOT SUBDUE ANGULIMALA WITH ALL MY STRENGTH AND YOU HAVE WON HIM WITHOUT LIFTING YOUR LITTLE FINGER. WE ARE GRATEFUL TO YOU, LORD.

THEN, SALUTING ANGULIMALA, THE KING LEFT.

ANGULIMALA BECAME DEVOTED TO BUDDHA. HE LISTENED TO THE MASTER'S WORDS OF WISDOM.

HE NURSED THE SICK.

I AM FEELING BETTER NOW, ANGULIMALA. YOU MAY REST.

DON'T MIND ME, BROTHER. YOU SLEEP.

ONE DAY WHEN ANGULIMALA WENT TO BEG FOR HIS FOOD.

DO YOU WANT MORE RICE?

YOU ARE GENEROUS, MY CHILD. MAY YOU, YOUR MOTHER AND FATHER BE BLESSED.

THAT ANGULIMALA HAD SUDDENLY BECOME DESPON-DENT DID NOT ESCAPE THE NOTICE OF BUDDHA.

WHY ARE YOU SO SAD, MY SON?

MASTER, THESE HANDS OF MINE ARE STAINED WITH BLOOD. I AM A SINNER WITHOUT A FUTURE, WITHOUT HOPE!

WHY CHILD, REPENTANCE IS THE ONLY FIRE THAT IS CAPABLE OF BURNING SINS ALREADY COMMIT-TED. YOU ARE ON THE RIGHT PATH.

BLESS ME, MASTER. YOUR PRESENCE AND YOUR WORDS ARE SOOTHING.

BUT ANGULIMALA CONTINUED TO SUFFER.

FATHER, HOW LONG MUST ANGULIMALA SUFFER? CAN'T YOU EASE HIM OF HIS BURDEN?

ALL IN GOOD TIME, ANATHAPINDIKA.

THEN ONE DAY, BUDDHA TOOK ANGULIMALA WITH HIM ON HIS ROUNDS. AS THEY PROCEEDED—

OH, GOD! I CAN'T BEAR IT...AH!... OOH!...

MASTER, SOMEONE SEEMS TO BE IN PAIN. LET US HURRY.

WHAT'S THE TROUBLE, MOTHER?

MY DAUGHTER IS ABOUT TO DELIVER A BABY, SIR. WE WERE ON OUR WAY TO TOWN.

CAN'T YOU ALLEVIATE HER MISERY, MASTER?

MOTHER, I AM DYING.

MY SON, BLESS THE WOMAN AND SAY: "WHEN I KILLED PEOPLE, I DID SO OUT OF IGNORANCE. IF I SPEAK THE TRUTH, LET THE WOMAN GET WELL."

BUT MASTER...

OH, SIR, DON'T SAY NO! PLEASE DON'T! SAVE HER.

WITH MUCH RELUCTANCE, ANGULIMALA OBEYED HIS MASTER'S ORDERS.

HOW CAN I, A RUTHLESS MURDERER, SAVE HER?

I DON'T KNOW IF I HAD KILLED WITH FULL KNOWLEDGE. IF I AM CORRECT IN SAYING SO, LET THIS WOMAN GET WELL.

AND THE TWO RESUMED THEIR JOURNEY. SUDDENLY —

OH, SIR, PLEASE WAIT.

IT'S THE OLD WOMAN. HER DAUGHTER MUST BE DYING.

THE OLD WOMAN APPEARED, BRINGING NEWS NOT OF DEATH, BUT OF LIFE.

SIR, YOU BLESSED MY DAUGHTER AND SAVED HER LIFE. BLESS HER LITTLE SON, TOO.

MOTHER, MERCIFUL BUDDHA WILL BLESS HIM.

I WANT BOTH OF YOU TO BLESS THE CHILD.

THE MASTER AND THE DISCIPLE BLESSED THE CHILD.

WHEN THE OLD WOMAN WENT AWAY—

ANGULIMALA, AT LEAST NOW ARE YOU CONVINCED THAT YOU HAVE OVERCOME YOUR PAST DEEDS?

I AM, MASTER, THANKS TO YOU.

SON, YOU NO LONGER NEED ME. YOU MUST WALK ALONE IN THE WORLD.

IF YOU INSIST, I WILL. BUT IT IS YOU WHO HAVE GIVEN ME THE STRENGTH TO DO SO. BUDDHAM SHARANAM GACCHAMI.*

AFTER PARTING FROM BUDDHA, ANGULIMALA DECIDED TO GO TO SHRAVASTI. AS HE ENTERED THE CITY —

LOOK! DID YOU RECOGNISE HIM?

WHY? HE IS JUST A COMMON MONK. OR IS HE A GREAT ONE?

* I TAKE REFUGE IN BUDDHA

ARMING THEMSELVES, A FURIOUS MOB APPROACHED ANGULIMALA.

LOOK! A CHILD HAS COME OUT TO OFFER RICE TO THE MONSTER IN DISGUISE.

HE IS GOING TO STRANGLE THAT CHILD.

NO, HE IS KISSING IT! STRANGE!

AS SOON AS ANGULIMALA STEPPED OUT OF THE HOUSE, A STONE HIT HIM ON THE FOREHEAD.

IT WAS FOLLOWED BY MANY MORE.

THEN THE MOB LET LOOSE ITS PENT-UP FURY.

HIT HIM HARD!

GIVE ME A CHANCE. IT'S MY TURN NOW.

WHAT DOES IT FEEL LIKE? WHY DON'T YOU FIGHT BACK?

BUT ANGULIMALA DID NOT RAISE A FINGER TO PROTECT HIMSELF.

SEVERLY BEATEN UP, HE STARTED CRAWLING TOWARDS THE ABODE OF HIS MASTER.

MAY YOU DIE A DOG'S DEATH.

WHEN HE REACHED THE MONASTERY—

ANGULIMALA, MY CHILD!

BUDDHAM... SHARANAM.. GA..CCHAA..MI*

*I TAKE REFUGE IN BUDDHA

DO YOU FEEL BETTER, MY CHILD?

NEVER BEFORE HAVE I FELT BETTER THAN I DO NOW, MASTER.

WERE YOU ANGRY WHEN THEY BEAT YOU UP?

NO, FATHER. WHEN I KILLED PEOPLE, I DID NOT KNOW WHAT I WAS DOING. SIMILARLY, THEY TOO DID NOT KNOW WHAT THEY WERE DOING.

ARE YOU AT REST NOW?

YES, FATHER. I AM AT PEACE WITH THE WORLD.

AND ANGULIMALA BREATHED HIS LAST.

ANGULIMALA WAS A GREAT SOUL. HE CONQUERED VICE, CRUELTY AND ANGER. HE HAS ATTAINED NIRVANA.